TYNE & WEAR AT WORK

Peter Hepplewhite

Published by Newcastle City Libraries & Arts in association with Tyne & Wear Archives Service

(Front cover) Looking up the berth at Armstrong's Elswick yards in 1889, the framework of this double-hulled battleship is vividly shown. The plating has barely started. A rivet heater's fire can be picked out just right of centre. Some of the beams for the whaleback deck are in position. This gave extra strength and helped waves wash over the ship in stormy weather.

Tyne & Wear Archives Services and Newcastle City Libraries & Arts wish to thank the following for their assistance in compiling this booklet:

Mrs V. Dobson
Booker Seeds Ltd.
NEI Parsons Ltd.
Mr J. Allison
Merz & McLellan, Consulting Engineers
Port of Sunderland Authority

Text and compilation by Peter Hepplewhite with the kind assistance of Joe Clarke and Richard Potts.

Published by Newcastle upon Tyne City Libraries & Arts, 1991.

ISBN 0902653 81 4

INTRODUCTION

The photographs in this volume have been compiled from the extensive collections of business records held by Tyne and Wear Archives Service. They illustrate the collections for the approximate period 1880 - 1920 and reflect the heavy industrial base of the North East. Above all they are a tribute to a workforce that earned a living from manufacturing. These four decades can serve as both inspiration and warning, as the area continues the painful task of rebuilding its industrial structure in the 1990s.

Between 1880 and 1920 the river corridors of the Tyne and the Wear hummed with activity. Their wealth was based largely on mining and the coal trade, shipbuilding and repairing, and engineering. Generally these were years of confidence and growth. A later writer caught the spirit of the times in this description of the Tyne:

Everywhere, from the dancing waters of the harbour, to the ebb and flow of the throbbing city, industry, resource and expansion, coal staithes, shipyards, engine shops, dry docks, chemical works, forges, electric lighting laboratories, warehouses, merchant offices, steamships, railway trains without end, without number, from Shields to Scotswood there is not its like in 13 miles of river the world over. [W. Richardson, *History of the Parish of Wallsend*, 1923]

The population soared. Between the census dates of 1881 and 1921 the figures for Newcastle, Gateshead and South Shields almost doubled. For every 100 people in Northumberland and Durham in 1881 there were 171 in 1921, a growth significantly higher than the 46% average for England and Wales.

The expansion of the coal industry underpinned the region's wealth. In 1886, 34 million tons were mined, rising to 52 million tons in 1906. In 1901 there were 37,000 miners in Northumberland, 15% of the total workforce and 100,000 in Durham, almost a quarter of the working population. In the years around the turn of the century coal shipments were buoyant, some 17 million tons from the Tyne alone. Of this over two-thirds was exported, with Germany, France and Italy the major customers.

The demand for colliers helped the development of the shipyards. The launch by Palmer's of the *John Bowes* in 1852 marked a turning point. This iron-built, screw-driven collier was the first modern cargo ship and an irrevocable step in the move from wood to iron vessels. By 1900 Britain dominated the international shipbuilding trade, launching more than half the world's tonnage. Of this more than half came from the North East. There were many famous shipyards and shipbuilders. Armstrong's at Elswick became the pre-eminent naval yard. The company's close links with the Royal Navy led many foreign governments to place orders.

Warships built for the Japanese Navy for example, became a familiar sight on the Tyne. Except for the Great War the output of the Wear was almost exclusively merchant ships. Doxford's became renowned for their adventurous design, the turret deck steamer, a standardised cargo ship. Laing's took a lead in the new field of oil tankers. A pinnacle was reached in 1906 when more than a million tons were launched on the Tyne, Wear and Tees. This included the majestic *Mauretania*, with marine engines of almost three-quarters of a million horsepower.

Shipbuilding also led to a host of subsidiary industries locally, and innovation abounded. After important experiments at Wallsend in the 1880s, mild steel was used for marine boilers, and a little later for ships' hulls. Wallsend-designed triple expansion engines became the workhorses of the merchant marine.

In 1884 Charles Parsons made the strategic inventions of the steam turbine and high-speed generator. These opened the way to the widespread use of electricity and a major new industry. Five years later Parsons opened the Heaton works and in 1900 supplied the first 1000 kw generating set to Elberfeld, Germany. Such was the massive progress of this period that by 1912 a 25,000 kw set was shipped to Chicago.

Parsons' efforts were re-inforced by Charles Merz who set up in Newcastle, and by Alphonse Reyrolle, a Frenchman who founded his switchgear works at Hebburn. Electricity, at first principally used for lighting, provided for example the electric tram, a major advance in town transport. This was reflected in the jump from a mere 26 men employed in Newcastle Tramways in 1881, to 669 men and 19 women in 1911.

Generally, work was readily available for skilled men. In the late 1880s an industrial handbook for Tyneside could boast that a man's wage was equivalent to that of a family working in the mills of Lancashire or Yorkshire. Certainly in engineering and shipbuilding workers earned wages as great as any other area except London. Overall, in about 1906 men in engineering earned 35s. 8d. (£1.74) per week; this was less than London's 38s. (£1.90) but 10% more than the national average of 32s .11d. (£1.65). Similarly in the shipyards the local average was 40s. 5d. (£2.02) compared with 35s. 11d.(£1.80) nationally.

Industrial work for women was markedly absent in the region, but slowly increasing. On Wearside paper mills and roperies offered some opportunities, for example Hendon Paper Works employed 150 women in 1900. New industries, such as electrical manufacturing provided further openings. In 1911 150 women worked with 1,396 males in making electrical apparatus in Newcastle. However, domestic service remained the most likely employment for an unmarried girl. There were more than 7,100 such servants in Newcastle in 1881 and 4,500 in Sunderland, and the numbers had hardly changed 30 years later. The Great War brought unprecedented demand for female labour, with government orders ensuring full employment and prosperity for the North East. When the conflict ended in 1918 there was a brief burst of activity with the need to replace wartime ship losses, but this did not last long. Increasing foreign competition and fluctuating world trading conditions were to expose long-term weaknesses.

Even during the years of expansion the area had been subjected to periodic short depressions. In 1909 for example the *Sunderland Year Book* declared:

Last year was one of continued depression in the shipbuilding and allied trades – the worst in fact for twenty-two years.

The region's economy had become too dependent on a few sectors of industry which in turn relied on healthy export markets. Wearside exemplified the problems. Shipbuilding and marine engineering provided over one third of all male jobs. By 1931 two-thirds of the unemployed in Sunderland were from these industries.

The year 1936 presented a grim contrast with 1906. The North East was no longer a vibrant and expanding region. The talk was of retrenchment and rationalisation, with designation as a 'Special Area' needing government help.

Industry is not just about products; it concerns people too. Group works' photographs, very often of a particular trade, reflected a regard for work that went beyond the pay packet. The results of their labour showed the skills of the hand, the judgement of eye and intelligence, the craft experience, as well as the sheer muscular energy required. They were men – and women – who could nurse sometimes ancient machines to produce mostly heavy goods that sold throughout the world.

It is these people who now take a bow.

Armstrong's shipyard at Elswick opened in 1884. The first warship to be built there, the Austrian fast cruiser *Panther*, is on the stocks. The photographer is standing on King's Meadows, the largest island in the Tyne. This was dredged away during the late 1880s to ease access to, and launches from, Armstrong's.

The ram bow is held in position as the keel is laid for *HMS Renown*, 1888. The Elswick yard's first battleship, she was renamed *HMS Victoria* and completed in 1890. Her career came to a tragic end in collision with *HMS Camperdown* off Syria three years later. The pile-driver seen working in the background sank hundreds of piles under the shipyard to spread the weight during building.

The *Crown of Germany* was a steel-hulled, four-masted barque built in 1892 at Belfast. In this view she is raised on a pontoon at Smith's Dock, North Shields, probably for refitting, c1900. At this time the company was the largest ship-repairing concern in the world.

Dobson's was a small family yard at Wincomblee, Walker on the Tyne.
They established a reputation for high-quality small vessels. Here the
work of a busy yard is vividly shown, with paddle steamers on the stocks.
The year is 1897.

Doxford's yard at Pallion, Sunderland was the largest on the Wear. The company established a formidable reputation for innovation with turret ships in the 1890s and the Doxford diesel engine in the 1920s. During the First World War they built 21 torpedo-boat destroyers for the Admiralty. This view shows TBDs under construction in 1915.

From 14-17 June 1917, King George V and Queen Mary made a tour of
North East coast factories and shipyards. The tour was marked by its
unprecedented informality. 1917 was a hard, disillusioning year in the
Great War and the royal visit a boost to flagging morale. Queen Mary is
seen here leaving the Oil Engine Department at Doxford's, Sunderland.

RISING SUN PIT.
WALLSEND.

J.S. GILL.
11/10/09.

Coal raised in Wallsend in the early nineteenth-century was famous for its quality. The name was adopted across the country, thus 'Yorkshire Wallsends' and 'Cardiff Wallsends' held high prices. The first series of pits at Wallsend closed due to flooding in 1854. The new 'Rising Sun' pit began drawing coal in 1908. The inset picture shows the boys in the workforce.

Photograph taken at Seghill Colliery,
Northumberland. Dec 12th 1923.

This photograph was a publicity shot for the North Eastern Electricity
Supply Company. The firm had pioneered the use of electricity for
industry, a process which accelerated in the 1920s. Here an electrically-
operated coal cutter is in use.

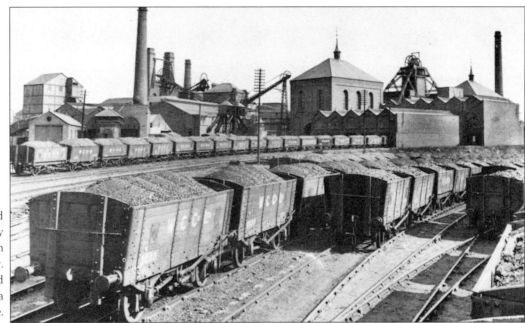

The Wearmouth Coal Company owned two pits in Sunderland, Wearmouth Colliery sunk in the 1830s and Hylton opened in 1899. High-quality gas coal was a speciality. This was shipped to gas companies in and around Britain and exported to Scandinavia and France.

Coal exports were a key part of Wearside's economy. Sunderland was the natural port for most of the Durham coalfield. Here an Italian steamer, *Caterina Gerolimich*, is loading at Wearmouth Staithes, c1925.

In the Great Northern Coalfield fireclay lay in abundance underneath the coal measures. This meant the raw material was cheap and many collieries ran brickworks. Priestman's collieries bought out Cowan's Firebrick Works at Blaydon Burn in 1900. This view shows the Hot End of a Sutcliff Trolley Brick Dryer, c1913. Each trolley held 250 bricks.

Customers included Consett Iron Works which ordered 20,000 bricks a week.

Quarrying was another major extractive industry in the area. Here the work force of Brunton Quarry, Gosforth is shown, c1890. In the background are stocks of newly-cut grindstones. Brunton's most famous order was the stone for the High Level Bridge, Newcastle, delivered in the 1840s.

JAN.18.1889.

No.3 Gates allowed access at high tide into the South Docks at the mouth of the Wear. This view shows construction work in 1889 when the entrance was being widened. One of the caissons holding back the water can be clearly seen at the back of the photograph. The gates were built from greenheart. This now-rare wood had a compressive strength greater than concrete and a natural oil highly resistant to salt water. It is also poisonous, requiring great care when cutting the timber. The gates were opened by a double-acting, water-powered hydraulic system.

THE HENDON PAPER WORKS COMPANY LTD
SUNDERLAND.

MAKERS OF
E.S.&T.S. WRITINGS,
FINE PRINTINGS,
TINTEDS ETC.
FOR HOME & EXPORT.

OVID

Hendon Paper Works at Grangetown, Sunderland, were opened in 1872 by Mr Bell, an iron founder from Tynemouth. By 1900 it had the largest paper mill in the region, producing 190 tons a week, with a workforce of 430, including 150 women. The inset photograph shows the discharge of esparto grass, a major ingredient for certain papers, at South Docks, Sunderland.

Sunderland was one of the main harbours for importing timber. The Durham collieries had an insatiable demand for pit props. In 1901 the River Wear Commissioners reported shipments running at between 500,000 and 700,000 dozen per year. This view shows pit props being discharged at South Docks, c1925.

This plate-bending machine is shown in use at Doxford's, c1905. Strengthening pieces for the honeycomb construction of a double-bottomed hull are being crimped (shaped).

These relatively-small turbine machines were built for the torpedo boat destroyer, *HMS Shark*, by Wallsend Slipway and Engineering Co. The inset photograph shows *Shark* on trial at 28 knots on 29 October 1912. Wallsend Slipway were renowned marine-engine builders. Their most famous order was for twenty-three boilers, each weighing 110 tons, for the Cunard liner *Mauretania*.

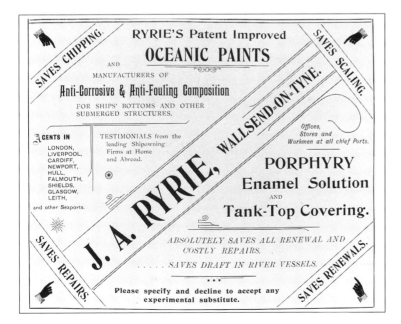

Shipbuilding led to a host of smaller subsidy industries servicing the needs of the yards. These advertisements, printed in 1901 in *The Syren and Shipping*, speak for themselves.

The Linkleter's Patent Ship-Fitting company opened in Percy Street, North Shields in 1882. Its most successful product was the self-levelling accomodation ladder. The firm's life rafts were in great demand, especially during the First World War, as an alternative or addition to lifeboats. These photographs were taken c1910.

LINKLETER'S PATENT
SHIP FITTINGS
COY., LIMITED.
NORTH SHIELDS.

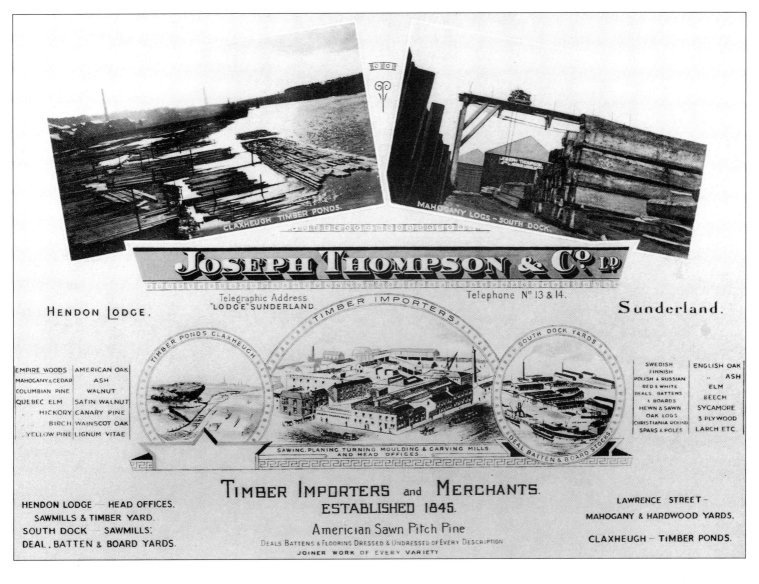

Thompson's was one of several major timber suppliers on the Wear.
This advertisement from the 1920s shows a tempting variety of now-rare
woods brought into the river.

Sunderland fish-quay is shown here, c1895. At that time the quay was located at the South Docks. During the mid-nineteenth century the Sunderland Fleet had supplied much of the County Durham trade, but by the end of the century was in relative decline. The River Wear Commissioners charged a steam trawler 3s. 6d. (17½ p) each landing, with extra dues of 3d. (1½ p) per thousand for herrings and 2d. (1p) per thousand for mackerel.

Farming was a major employer in the Tyne and Wear area in the years before the Second World War. This unidentified harvest scene was taken by Finney's Seeds, c1920. The company was an important provider of agricultural and horticultural seeds. The nurseries and trial grounds were at Stocksfield, with shops in Newcastle and Sunderland.

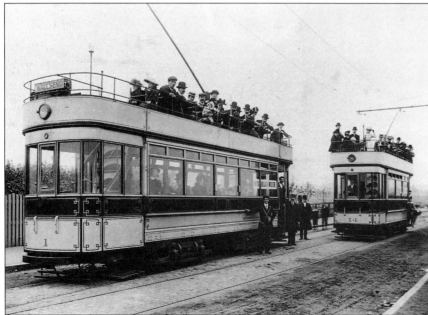

Tyneside Tramways and Tramroads Co. Ltd took delivery of its first electric trams in 1902. These photographs record the speed and hill-climbing tests conducted by the consulting engineer, Charles Merz. A tram with eight to twelve passengers could reach 13.6mph running with the slope down Howden Road. The hill climb on Church Bank, Wallsend, was a measured 500 feet, half of this on a gradient of 1 in 11. Here the trams managed 6.8mph.

Combined shunting locomotives and mobile cranes were produced by several locomotive builders in the area for use inside steel works, shipyards and other heavy engineering plants. R. & W. Hawthorn Leslie & Co. Ltd of the Forth Banks works in Newcastle produced a distinctive design which featured a vertical extension at the rear of the boiler to form a large steam cylinder; this provided the 'derricking' action for the crane jib. The crane hook was fixed on the jib and the whole arrangement could be 'slewed' by a small steam engine which engaged a toothed ring fixed around the top of the boiler.

The locomotive in this photograph was one of three which were used around the Forth Banks works between 1891 and its closure in 1960.

The express from Leeds left the line on the afternoon of Tuesday, 26 March 1907. The accident happened just outside Felling Station. The train was running at about 30mph and the engine burrowed halfway into the embankment. Eight passengers were seriously injured and two subsequently died. The breakdown gang from Gateshead was on the scene within half an hour and the line reopened by Friday.

Richardson's Leather Works was a fine Quaker family business. Isaac
and William Richardson set up in Elswick in 1780. The company was
carried on by eight generations of the family until its closure in 1972. The
belt shop is shown here in 1898. The bowler-hatted foreman, Mr Kelly,
keeps a strict eye on production.

The Elswick Lead Works cooperage made and repaired barrels for the sale of powdered lead. Dry lead was used in the manufacture of protective paints for ships and bridges. This photograph was taken c1890.

The hard task of splicing a steel rope, c1920, is shown here at Webster's Ropery, Deptford, Sunderland. Webster's had a reputation for pioneering new technology. Established in 1793 they were the first to make fibre ropes by machine. The company was producing iron-wire ropes by 1843 and was amongst the first to supply steel-wire ropes. One order which literally brought Sunderland to a standstill began its journey to Whitehaven Colliery in Cumbria in 1892. The twenty-five ton, steel, haulage rope was four miles long. It took thirty horses to move the load to the Goods Station at Monkwearmouth.

In 1913 Armstrong-Whitworth's set up their Aviation department. By 1918 they turned out some ninety aeroplanes a month from their factory on Grandstand Road, Gosforth. With an eye to a good photograph an Armstrong car has been driven from the Scotswood works.

By 1913 Armstrong-Whitworth's was the premier British armaments manufacturer. That year the company boasted a workforce of 25,000 and a wages bill of £38,500 per month. By 1918 employees numbered 78,000 and the firm had expanded across the Tyne. In the first photograph a rail load of tanks leaves the Close Works at Gateshead, c1917. After the war the plant specialised in large castings, each up to thirty-two tons in weight.

Alphonse Constant Reyrolle started his Hebburn Works in 1901. The company pioneered the development of electrical switchgear. A notable achievement was the design of metal-clad draw-out switchgear, developed for the Tyneside supply industry and adopted nationally. A machine shop and female assembly workers can be seen here, c1910.

Charles Parsons started up his Heaton Works on a two-acre site in 1889.
Over the next ten years the company established the steam turbine as the
standard prime-mover for power stations. By 1914 the firm employed
1200. The female labour shown here became an essential part of the
workforce during the Great War. As Lady Parsons wrote in 1918: *There is
no doubt that many women developed great mechanical skill and a real love of
their work.*

Portions of condensers from a 50,000 kw turbo alternator leave Parson's
Heaton Works c1920. They are bound for a power station in Chicago.